Y0-ABD-839

Retold by Tim and Jenny Wood

 First published in the United States in 1991 by Grosset & Dunlap, Inc., a member of The Putnam & Grosset Book Group, New York. Published simultaneously in Canada. Printed and bound in Singapore. ISBN 0-448-40145-2

MY FAIRY TALE LIBRARY

SNOW WHITE AND THE SEVEN DWARFS

Publishers • GROSSET & DUNLAP • New York

There was once a beautiful princess called Snow White. After her mother died, her father married again. His new Queen was very vain. Every day she looked in her magic mirror and said, "*Mirror, mirror on the wall, who is the fairest of them all?*" Every day the mirror replied, "*You, O Queen, are the fairest of all.*"

As the years passed, Snow White grew more and more beautiful. The day came when the Queen's magic mirror gave her a different answer: "*You are fair, O Queen, it's true, but Snow White is fairer now than you.*" The Queen was furious and decided that Snow White must die.

The Queen ordered her huntsman to take Snow White into the forest. He was to kill her and bring back her heart, to prove she was dead.

The huntsman led Snow White deep into the forest, but when he drew his knife, Snow White begged him to spare her life.

The huntsman saw Snow White's tears and he took pity on her.

"I cannot kill you," he told Snow White. But he made her promise never to return home.

On his way back to the palace, the huntsman killed a deer. He cut out its heart and took this to the Queen, telling her Snow White was dead.

Snow White wandered through the forest, lost and alone. At last she came upon a cottage. She tapped on the door, then went inside.

There she saw a long, low table laid with seven places. Snow White was so hungry that she took some bread and cheese. Upstairs, she found seven little beds. She was so tired that she snuggled into one and fell asleep.

The cottage was the home of seven dwarfs. Every morning they went to a nearby mine and dug for diamonds. Every evening they returned home carrying their shovels, pickaxes, and bags full of jewels.

As soon as the dwarfs arrived home that night, they saw that someone had been in their house and eaten some of their food. So they began to search the cottage.

When they went upstairs, they found Snow White asleep.

"Who is this beautiful girl?" they whispered to one another in amazement.

Snow White awoke with a start. But seeing that the dwarfs were friendly and kind, she told them her story. The dwarfs felt so sorry for Snow White that they invited her to stay with them.

"But you must never open the door to anyone while we're away at the mine," they warned her. "If the wicked Queen finds out that you're alive, she may try to kill you."

Snow White was very happy looking after the dwarfs.

The Queen, meanwhile, believing that Snow White was dead, had not asked the magic mirror her usual question. But one day, as she was brushing her hair, the Queen idly said,

"Mirror, mirror on the wall, who is the fairest of them all?" And the mirror promptly replied, *"You, O Queen, are fair, it's true, but Snow White is fairer far than you. Deep within the greenwood shade, Snow White with dwarfs her home has made."*

The Queen flew into a rage. Realizing that the huntsman had tricked her, she decided to kill Snow White herself.

Disguised as an old peddler woman, the Queen went to the dwarfs' cottage. There she found Snow White sitting by the window.

"Would you like to buy a pretty comb for your hair?" asked the Queen in her sweetest voice.

Forgetting the dwarfs' warning, Snow White opened the door. The Queen showed her a golden comb.

"Let me put this comb in your hair," offered the Queen. But the comb had been dipped in deadly poison. As soon as the teeth touched Snow White's head, she fell down as if dead. The Queen ran off laughing triumphantly.

That evening, when the dwarfs returned, they found Snow White lying on the ground with the poisoned comb in her hair. They snatched it out, and as they did so, Snow White opened her eyes.

The dwarfs realized that the peddler woman must have been the wicked Queen in disguise. Once again they begged Snow White never to open the door to strangers.

As soon as the Queen returned home, she rushed to ask, "*Mirror, mirror on the wall, who is the fairest of them all?*" The mirror replied, "*O Queen, your poison was in vain, for Snow White is alive again.*"

In a furious temper, the Queen disguised herself once more, this time as a peasant woman with a basket of apples. She placed the juiciest one on top. It had been dipped in poison.

"Who will buy my tasty apples?" called the Queen as she reached the cottage.

Snow White refused to open the door. But she thought that it would do no harm to open the window.

"Taste this one, pretty lady," offered the Queen, holding out the poisoned apple. Snow White took one bite, then sank to the floor, dead.

The Queen rushed home. And this time when she spoke to her magic mirror, it gave her the answer that she wanted. *"You, O Queen,"* the mirror replied, *"are the fairest of all."*

When the dwarfs came home that evening, they were horrified to find Snow White dead. They made a glass coffin and sadly laid her in it. The coffin was put among the flowers in their garden, where the dwarfs kept watch day and night.

Many weeks later a prince came riding through the forest. He saw Snow White lying in her glass coffin. She looked so beautiful that he fell in love with her at once. He asked the dwarfs if he could kiss her, and the dwarfs agreed.

As the Prince kissed Snow White, a piece of poisoned apple fell from her lips and her eyes opened. The moment she saw the handsome Prince, she fell in love with him.

The dwarfs were overjoyed that Snow White was alive again, and even happier when the Prince and Snow White decided to marry.

That day, when the Queen asked the mirror her favorite question, *"Mirror, mirror on the wall, who is the fairest of them all?"*, it replied, *"You, O Queen, are fair, it's true, but Snow White is fairer still than you."*

The Queen smashed the magic mirror in her rage. When it was discovered how she had tried to kill Snow White, she was banished from the land.

Snow White said good-bye to the dwarfs and rode away with her handsome Prince. They were soon married and lived happily ever after.